KIWI

NEW ZEALAND'S REMARKABLE BIRD

KIWI

NEW ZEALAND'S REMARKABLE BIRD

Neville Peat

GODWIT

Acknowledgements

Thanks are due to Hugh Robertson, Rogan Colbourne and John McLennan, leading lights in kiwi recovery work, for their information and advice. Valuable assistance also came from Chris Rickard, Selena Brown, Paul van Klink and Megan Hieatt at the frontline of Westland kiwi research and management work. Information on the latest developments in captive kiwi management was supplied by Tara Atkinson (Orana Wildlife Park), Eric Fox (Otorohanga Zoological Society), Ron Goudswaard (Wellington Zoo), Paul Wilson (Queenstown Kiwi and Birdlife Park) and Bruce Benseman (Nga Manu Nature Reserve).
For hospitality in South Westland I thank Dave and Margaret Bradley (Hannah's Clearing, Haast) and Suzy and Alex Miller (Waiho, Franz Josef).

A GODWIT BOOK
published by
Random House New Zealand
18 Poland Road, Glenfield, Auckland, New Zealand

First published 1999

ISBN 1 86962 046 1

Design: Grace Design
Cover photograph: Tui de Roy/Hedgehog House New Zealand
Back cover photograph: Tui de Roy/The Roving Tortoise
Cover design: Grace Design
Maps: Jonette Surridge
Prepress by MH Group, Auckland
Printed by South China Printing Company

Contents

Preface

As the twenty-first century begins, New Zealand's national bird is in trouble. Once a dominant force in the bird world on both main islands, the kiwi is now dwindling in number. Fewer than 80,000 remain whereas in pre-human times they numbered in the millions. Could the unthinkable occur — could the kiwi become extinct?

At the start of the 1990s, as New Zealand reached 150 years of nationhood, a number of books appeared in salute of the kiwi, among them *The Incredible Kiwi,* which I wrote to accompany a *Wild South* television documentary. At that time, a number of writers were sounding alarm bells. In *The Incredible Kiwi* I observed:

> Until recent times kiwi conservation was rarely an issue. The kiwi was thought to be holding its own, by and large, against predators, and few people took much notice of matters such as its range and population densities. Times are changing. To be sure, the kiwi grows up in a school of hard knocks and copes up to a point, but if its numbers and range continue to contract, special measures will be required to save it.

After decades of complacency and minimal research, kiwi conservation emerged as a compelling wildlife issue in the 1990s. In 1991 the Department of Conservation, in partnership with the Bank of New Zealand and Royal Forest and Bird Protection Society, launched the first Kiwi Recovery Plan (1991–1996), heralding increased commitment to protecting the various kinds of kiwi. The research effort took a decisive leap forward. So did public awareness of the teetering plight of kiwi. The research on both main islands confirmed the worst — the kiwi was in retreat. Kiwi numbers were declining at an alarming rate; birds were disappearing from fringe areas. A second Kiwi Recovery Plan, spanning the 10 years to 2006, calls for a sustained effort on research and protection measures.

The 1990s have produced much new information on the various kinds of kiwi. Six varieties (taxa) are now recognised, with perhaps more to be identified as research proceeds. Besides the advances in genetic analysis, we now know more about how kiwi differ from one another, where they live, how they behave, the constraints on breeding and the hazards they face. This book is an update of the knowledge gleaned from the Kiwi Recovery Plan work — precious knowledge gathered by those who work in kiwi habitats that are often remote, inconvenient and uncomfortable and those who work with kiwi in captivity. More than anything, it is hoped the book will help spread the word on the kiwi's predicament.

The kiwi's distinctive call — representing in New Zealand the call of the wild — has become a desperate cry for assistance. The kiwi is a celebrity bird. It has an

honoured place in the indigenous and modern cultures of New Zealand despite the fact that the vast majority of New Zealanders have never seen or even heard their national bird in the wild. In the past we have taken the kiwi for granted. Today, it is clearer than ever that we do so at risk of the kiwi's extinction on the main islands of New Zealand.

Neville Peat
Broad Bay
Otago Peninsula

Above: A little spotted kiwi on Kapiti Island.

7

A real character

The kiwi commands a unique place in the world of birds. Picture a shaggy, burrowing, whiskered creature that prowls the forest floor at night sniffing out its food. In a land devoid of terrestrial mammals save two species of bat, the kiwi acts out the role of a small mammal — a badger, for example, or perhaps an ant-eater.

The kiwi is in fact the nearest thing to an animal in the bird world — a biological oddity. It is a bird without a tail or wings, with hair-like feathers that resemble fur and it is oddly pear-shaped with a mole-like head. Imagine the kiwi head minus its bill. The shape, fluffiness and long whiskers are very animal-like.

The kiwi is unquestionably an offshoot in the evolutionary story of birds. Found only in New Zealand, it is living proof of the lengths to which birds will go to adapt to their habitats and circumstances. Kiwi ancestry spans millions of years. No one knows for sure whether its distant ancestors flew but clearly the kiwi lost the power of flight eons ago and retains only pathetically small wing bones, roughly the size of the outer two joints of a child's little finger. To compensate for flightlessness, it has developed stout and powerful legs, toes and claws that together account for up to a third of its bodyweight. It is a superb runner and fights with flashing razor-sharp claws.

Biologically, the kiwi sets several world records. Of all the kiwi's improbable features, perhaps the most bizarre, for a

Kiwi Eccentricities

Kiwi	Most Birds	Most Mammals
Hair-like plumage	Feathers	Hair
No tail; vestigial wings	Tail, wings	Tail, no wings
Long whiskers	No whiskers	Whiskers
Marrow-filled bones	Air-filled bones	Marrow-filled bones
Heavy, powerful legs and feet	Light, delicate legs and feet	Powerful legs and feet
Both ovaries functional	Only one ovary works	Both ovaries functional
Large ear openings	Small concealed ears	Large ear openings
Blood temperature of 38˚C	Blood temperature of about 40˚C	Blood temperature of about 38˚C

A great spotted kiwi, North-west Nelson.

bird, is its sense of smell. It is renowned for its 'nose'. It has a well-developed sense of smell because the part of the brain controlling this sense (the olfactory bulb) is much larger than in other birds and rather more like a mammal's in structure.

But the best-known feature of kiwi physiology is the egg, which is improbably, outrageously large. It is equivalent to six hen's eggs. It can weigh up to a fifth of the female's bodyweight. The egg is inordinately large, so the theory goes, because the kiwi's ancestors were themselves bigger-bodied, topping 12 kg. The kiwi body may have shrunk to fill the forest floor niche but there was little reduction in the size of its egg.

The animal-like whiskers, or rictal bristles, of the kiwi help it navigate at night — a form of short-range radar. Despite its small beady eyes, the kiwi sees reasonably well.

The kiwi's blood temperature is about 38°C, two degrees lower than most birds and nearer that of mammalian blood. And the kiwi, like a mammal, has marrow-filled bones. Flighted birds have lightweight bones filled with air-sacs — unnecessary for a bird that has all its requirements met at ground level.

The kiwi possibly developed a nocturnal habit to avoid falling victim to large raptors that are now extinct and also because invertebrate food was in better supply at night. The kiwi found itself in a land without predatory mammals and so it became flightless. In New Zealand, flightlessness is something of a fashion among birds. Several different birds abandoned flight here. Living examples include kakapo and takahe. Several other species are weakly flighted.

Left: A North Island brown kiwi, with its huge egg, which is 20 percent of its bodyweight.

For a host of reasons, therefore, the kiwi took the plunge and filled a niche in the New Zealand forest as a nocturnal feeder, territorial and highly mobile, cryptically coloured and hidden by day. It adopted the role, more or less, of a mammal.

The kiwi's unusual, almost freakish nature was emphasised some years ago by the visit of an American ecologist and evolutionary biologist, William A. Calder, of the University of Arizona. Dr Calder studied, in particular, the kiwi egg, its physical properties, incubation requirements, and the significance of its size. He developed a huge respect for the kiwi, and paid it this compliment: 'I award this remarkable bird the status of an honorary mammal.'

Certainly the kiwi has created biological records. The kiwi's character shines out, too — gritty, strident, toilsome and not unused to hard knocks. It is a bird of real character. Not surprisingly, it has become an icon, and its image is now inseparable from 'New Zealandness'.

It is, however, surprising that kiwi numbers are declining everywhere except on offshore island sanctuaries despite the fact that kiwi have had full legal protection throughout the twentieth century. Ironically, the rate of decline probably quickened following legal protection. Kiwi populations are estimated to have fallen by 95 percent through the twentieth century, mainly as a result of predators such as stoats, ferrets, cats and dogs — all animals introduced in the nineteenth century. Research work presents a dismal outlook for mainland kiwi unless conservation efforts are stepped up — and quickly.

An Okarito brown kiwi

An imported name?

Kiwi is the general Māori name for New Zealand's national bird. Although the name was once thought to represent the bird's loud contact call, it is clearly not a good imitation of the call, which in the great spotted and little spotted kiwi is more an ascending *'Crrruick!'* and in brown kiwi an ascending whistle that quickly tails off. It is more likely the name, kiwi, was imported from ancestral Māori homelands in the South Pacific, where a bird called kivi, the bristle-thighed curlew *Numenius tahitiensis,* probes tidal mudflats and reefs for marine worms and other food.

The kivi, smaller than the kiwi, has mottled brown plumage and a long downward-curving bill. Its resemblance to the flightless bird of the forest that Māori ancestors encountered on their arrival in Aotearoa was probably sufficient for the name to be transplanted. Māori applied many names of plants and animals familiar in their tropical island homelands to New Zealand counterparts or species that looked similar.

As the Māori language developed, the letter 'v' gave way to 'w', thus kivi (pronounced kee-vee) would naturally translate to kiwi in the same way as the flightless New Zealand rail known as weka is a bird similar to the veka (or ve'a) of tropical Polynesia.

The name tokoeka, now formally applied to southern brown kiwi, combines an echo of 'weka' with the name for a walking stick (toko).

Ratites

The kiwi is the smallest member of a group of flightless birds known as ratites, including the emu of Australia (below), the ostrich of Africa, the rhea of South America, the cassowary of Papua New Guinea and the extinct moa.

Ratites evolved alongside dinosaurs, before the break-up of the southern landmass called Gondwana about 80 million years ago. One theory holds that when Gondwana split up to create today's continents, the big-boned ratites rafted away with those vast disconnected slabs of the earth's crust and continued on separate evolutionary paths.

Kiwi share with the other ratites features such as a flat breastbone (the word, ratite, is derived from the Latin word, *ratis,* meaning a raft or unkeeled vessel). Most birds are equipped with a projecting breastplate to which strong muscles for flight are attached. The kiwi has the least-developed wing bones of the ratite group. The ostrich and the rhea, although flightless, use their vestigial wings for courtship displays. Ratites are further distinguished by their mouth structure. They have a double palate whereas all other birds have a single palate. There are skeletal affinities between kiwi and moa, and chromosome links have been demonstrated between kiwi and emus.

More kiwi faces

Kiwi are a surprisingly diverse lot. For decades, New Zealanders had little information about kiwi biology and behaviour. Myths abound: kiwi laid just one enormous egg per season; only the male parent incubated it; kiwi were said to bumble about the forest at night, somewhat pitiful figures tapping the ground like a blind person with a walking stick.

Kiwi research since the 1970s has exploded many misunderstandings. Depending on the species and where they live, kiwi are surprisingly variable in their habits.

In 1995, the kiwi world was redescribed. Genetic research identified four species rather than three as previously thought, and six varieties (or taxa) of kiwi. It is quite likely that some of the species will be further divided.

All kiwi share the genus name *Apteryx*, meaning wingless bird. The species names of the North Island brown, little spotted kiwi and great spotted kiwi recognise prominent nineteenth-century scientists and explorers; the southern tokoeka's species name, *australis,* simply means south.

Ornithologists have placed the six kiwi not only in a family by themselves, Apterygidae, but also in an order in which they are the only members, Apterygiformes — an uncommon distinction. This exclusive taxonomy reflects the unique nature of kiwi. It hints, too, at the extended evolutionary journey of kiwi upon a landmass far removed from any other and isolated for tens of millions of years.

Species	Variety (Taxa)
North Island brown *Apteryx mantelli*	North Island brown Okarito brown
Southern tokoeka *Apteryx australis*	Southern tokoeka Haast tokoeka
Little spotted *Apteryx owenii*	Little spotted
Great spotted *Apteryx haastii*	Great spotted

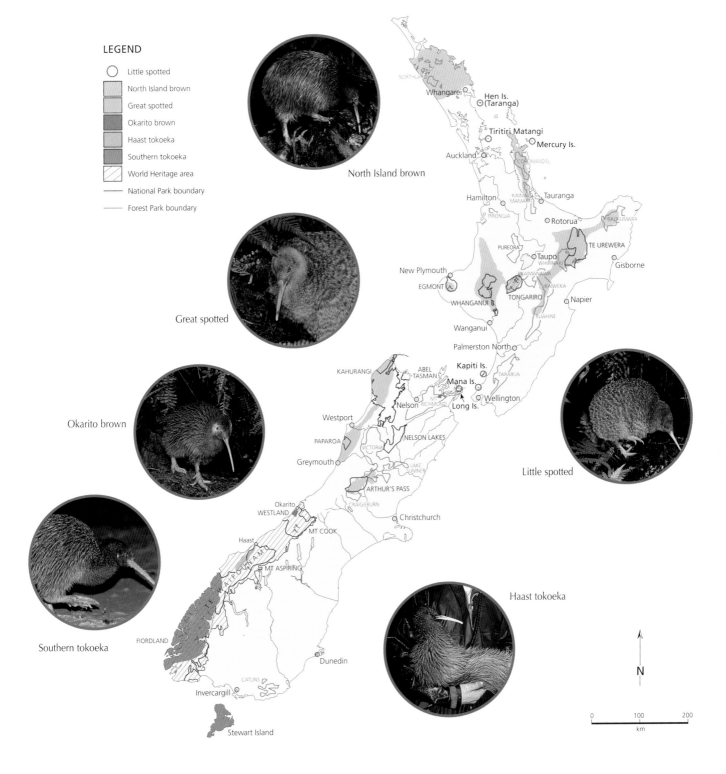

LEGEND

○ Little spotted
North Island brown
Great spotted
Okarito brown
Haast tokoeka
Southern tokoeka
World Heritage area
— National Park boundary
— Forest Park boundary

North Island brown

Great spotted

Okarito brown

Little spotted

Southern tokoeka

Haast tokoeka

Whangarei
Hen Is. (Taranga)
Tiritiri Matangi
Mercury Is.
Auckland
Hamilton
Tauranga
Rotorua
TE UREWERA
New Plymouth
Taupo
Gisborne
EGMONT
KAIMANAWA
Napier
WHANGANUI
TONGARIRO
Wanganui
Palmerston North
Kapiti Is.
KAHURANGI
ABEL TASMAN
Mana Is.
TARARUA
Westport
Nelson
MT RICHMOND
Long Is.
Wellington
PAPAROA
NELSON LAKES
Greymouth
VICTORIA
LAKE SUMNER
ARTHUR'S PASS
CRAIGIEBURN
Okarito
Christchurch
WESTLAND
MT COOK
Haast
MT ASPIRING
TE WAIPOUNAMU
FIORDLAND
Dunedin
CATLINS
Invercargill
Stewart Island

N

0   100   200
km

North Island brown kiwi

Apteryx mantelli 'North Island'

MĀORI NAMES: Kiwi nui, kiwi parure, kiwi kura

HEIGHT: 40 cm

AVERAGE WEIGHT: Female 2.8 kg, male 2.2 kg

DESCRIPTION: Reddish brown to dark brown feathers, streaked lengthways, with bristly plumage around the back of the neck and shoulders. The bill is ivory or light horn, its average length is 13 cm in females, and 10 cm in males. The iris is black. The legs and feet are grey-brown.

DISTRIBUTION: Northland, Coromandel, Little Barrier Island, Bay of Plenty and western Waikato, inland Taranaki, Urewera National Park, Kaweka, Ahimanawa and northern Ruahine Ranges

HABITAT: Native forest, forest margins, shrubland, exotic forest, rough farmland

STATUS: Endangered. The population is projected to halve in three generations.

North Island browns, the big-nosed northerners with spiky plumage, are the most widespread kiwi variety. Populations are scattered around the upper two-thirds of the island, with Northland harbouring the densest and largest population. Kiwi are relatively common in parts of Northland, where birds have spread into some pine plantations and through semi-developed farmland. In the Waipoua and Tangiteroria indigenous forests, densities can exceed 20 pairs per square kilometre (compared to, say, four pairs of great spotted kiwi per square kilometre

in upland areas of North-west Nelson). To the south, North Island browns have now disappeared from the lower third of the North Island, south of the 40 degree latitude line.

Regional variation has been observed in the North Island browns to the point where subspecies may one day be recognised. The North Island browns are divided into three main populations:

- Northland
- King Country/Taranaki/Whanganui
- Coromandel/Bay of Plenty/East Coast/Hawke's Bay.

Even within these regions there can be physical variation. To protect the regional variation, transfers of eggs and birds for management reasons from one region to another are not permitted.

A North Island brown might produce up to six eggs in a season. During incubation, the female generally stays in the nest for the first day then lets the male take over, by himself, right through to hatching. She will then get on with feeding and building up condition so a second egg can be laid in about three weeks, often in a burrow close to the first nest. Later in the year she may lay a second two-egg clutch, especially if the first clutch fails. She may even go on to produce, in a good year, a third clutch of one or two eggs. At about 430 g each, they will add up to almost her own weight. One North Island brown kiwi egg tipped the scales at 500 g.

Okarito brown kiwi
Apteryx mantelli 'Okarito'

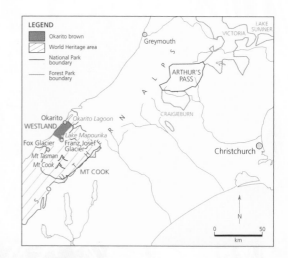

The Okarito brown kiwi, closely related to the North Island brown but generally smaller and greyer, and often distinguished by white feathering around head and face, live in an area between the Okarito and Waiho Rivers in Westland National Park.

Okarito brown kiwi number between 150 and 200. About half of them have white feathering, in patches, around their neck, head and face. White 'eyebrows' are

HEIGHT: 38 cm

AVERAGE WEIGHT: Female 2.7 kg, male 1.9 kg

DESCRIPTION: Slightly smaller than North Island brown kiwi, with soft grey-brown plumage and white patches common on the neck, head and face. The whiskers are shorter than those on the North Island brown. The bill is light brown or horn in colour, its average length is 12.5 cm in females, and 9.7 cm in males. The legs and feet are grey-brown.

DISTRIBUTION: Across 9800 hectares of South Okarito Forest in Westland National Park, between Waiho River and Okarito River

HABITAT: Lowland and coastal rainforest

STATUS: Critically endangered. The population is currently under 250.

common. Strangely, a significant number — more than a third — have eye defects, typified by what researchers call the 'poached egg' look. Even birds that appear totally blind with whitened eyes have maintained good condition.

They live in a squarish area of Westland National Park known as South Okarito Forest, roughly 10 km by 10 km and running down to the sea. The area is bounded by Lake Mapourika and a state highway on the inland side, the Okarito River in the north and the Waiho River in the south. Territories, distributed across most of the 9800 hectares in the block, reach about 100 hectares. This is at the larger end of territory size for kiwi anywhere — perhaps due to the low productivity of the wet, leached soils in the Okarito forest.

The isolation of Okarito brown kiwi from their North Island relatives is a puzzle. The ancestors of the Okarito

birds would have experienced a series of ice ages over the past two million years, with glaciers spilling west off the Southern Alps and covering much of the present-day forest. During the most extreme periods of glaciation, habitat suitable for kiwi would have been fragmented. Perhaps the Okarito brown kiwi became separated for thousands of years on a forested island surrounded by ice. The Okarito brown may, in time, be identified as a species in its own right. However, it is the most critically endangered of all kiwi at present.

Okarito brown kiwi eggs, which weigh about 400 g, carry a blue-green tinge. These kiwi lay up to three eggs a season between June and February, incubating one at a time through to hatching. The male tends to sit through the day and is relieved part-way through the night by the female bird. Okarito chicks generally remain longer with their parents — up to about four months — than do their North Island brown cousins.

Southern tokoeka

Apteryx australis 'Fiordland/Stewart Island'

MĀORI NAMES: Tokoeka, roa, rowi

HEIGHT: 40 cm

AVERAGE WEIGHT: Female 3 kg, male 2.3 kg

DESCRIPTION: Brown or grey-brown plumage, which is softer than that of the North Island brown kiwi. The bill is cream to pale pink, its average length is 13 cm in females, and 10 cm in males. The iris is black. The legs and feet are pale brown.

DISTRIBUTION: Fiordland (except far south) and Stewart Island.

HABITAT: Native forest, forest margins, subalpine shrubland, duneland

STATUS: Fiordland and Stewart Island populations vulnerable. The population is forecast to decline.

Tokoeka are scattered through much of Fiordland, although they are not found in the far south. This is surprising as the remote and richly forested nature of the area would seem well suited to supporting kiwi. Stewart Island is a tokoeka stronghold, however. The plumage of Stewart Island birds tends to be more rufous than that of Fiordland populations.

Scientists continue to puzzle over the reasons for the differences between the southern tokoeka and the Haast tokoeka. An unusual rock type known as ultramafic may be implicated in their separation. A belt of ultramafic rocks lies between Fiordland and South Westland. Perhaps the chemistry in these rocks, which produces stunted vegetation, set up a food barrier that kept the Haast and Fiordland populations separated.

Southern tokoeka males and females share incubation duties, although little is known about their nesting behaviour.

The naturalist Richard Henry, working in the 1800s, summed up the southern tokoeka well:

> No more perfect fit exists than that of the roas for their dominions. Their feathers . . . are amply warm and waterproof; and their skins are thick and oily as if to defy the everlasting damp of the shady forest, where they never feel a gleam of sunshine.

LEGEND

Southern tokoeka

World Heritage area

National Park boundary

Forest Park boundary

Haast tokoeka

Apteryx australis 'Haast'

HEIGHT: 40 cm

AVERAGE WEIGHT: Female 3 kg, male 2.5 kg

DESCRIPTION: Reddish brown plumage, streaked lengthways. The bill is cream to pale pink, its average length is 12 cm in females, and 9 cm long in males. The legs and feet are pale brown.

DISTRIBUTION: Haast region of South Westland, between Haast and Cascade Rivers, with greatest numbers on the Haast Range above the treeline

HABITAT: Lowland native forest to subalpine grassland

STATUS: Critically endangered. The population is currently under 250.

The Haast tokoeka, a variety of the southern tokoeka species, occur between the Haast and Cascade Rivers, with a significant number living at or above the treeline on the Haast Range, where they reach an altitude of 1500 m. They are separated from the Okarito brown kiwi by about 150 km of forested ranges interspersed with lakes, rivers and coastal flats. The Haast tokoeka is possibly a full species in its own right.

Some of the Haast tokoeka are lowlanders living in the forest at the foot of the range and some of them are mountaineers, surviving on the tussocky slopes and plateaus of the range. There are somewhere between 200 and 300 Haast tokoeka. They are not very accessible and quite spread out. Despite the harsher environment on the tops,

more Haast tokoeka are heard calling there than at the forested foot of the range.

Nonetheless, Haast tokoeka are declining in number in and around the Haast Range. In the mid-1900s they were reasonably common on the lowlands. They were seen on the Haast Pass highway, they visited huts in the bush, and they were heard calling reasonably often near the small settlements strung out along the road to Jackson Bay. Only occasionally are kiwi now reported from areas beyond the Haast Range and the land between the Waiatoto and Arawhata Rivers. Geographical names such as Apteryx Spur and Roa Spur on the Haast Range suggest it was a hot spot for kiwi in the past.

Haast tokoeka are known to lay mainly single-egg

clutches, repeated twice or even three times during a season. The birds living above the treeline on the Haast Range have a more severe climate to cope with. Their burrows, built in tussock grassland, are often buried under snow in August–September, when the first eggs are laid. Tunnels need to be dug through the snow for access.

Little spotted kiwi
Apteryx owenii

MĀORI NAME: Kiwi pukupuku

HEIGHT: 25 cm

AVERAGE WEIGHT: Female 1.3 kg, male 1.1 kg

DESCRIPTION: Grey plumage overall, mottled or banded transversely white, with a brownish or ginger tinge. The plumage is soft to touch. The bill is ivory to pale pink, its average length is 8.5 cm in females, and 7 cm in males. The iris is black. The legs and feet are cream to pale grey.

DISTRIBUTION: Offshore islands only — Kapiti Island, Hen Island (Taranga), Red Mercury Island (Whakau), Tiritiri Matangi Island, Mana Island, Long Island (Marlborough Sounds)

HABITAT: Coastal native forest and forest margins, shrubland

STATUS: Endangered. Forecast to increase in number but because of low population and small area, it is vulnerable.

The little spotted, smallest kiwi of all, is holding its own on six offshore islands. Kapiti Island is the stronghold for the species. About 1000 birds live on Kapiti and they have occupied virtually all of the suitable habitat. To spread the risk of extinction and ease the pressure on the Kapiti habitat, birds have been transferred to island sanctuaries elsewhere. Long Island in Queen Charlotte Sound received four birds in 1981. There are now at least 10 there. The population at Red Mercury Island (Whakau) off the Coromandel Peninsula was established with the transfer from Kapiti of 12 birds (six males and six females) in 1983. There are now 30 birds there, including probably 13 pairs. Hen Island (Taranga) off Northland's east coast, which received 38 birds from Kapiti in 1988–89, now has more than 50, and Tiritiri Matangi, a well-known bird sanctuary in the Hauraki Gulf, had as many as 25 birds in 1998 after receiving five pairs in 1993 and six more birds in 1995. Tiritiri Matangi can probably accommodate over 40 pairs.

Mana Island near Wellington is the home of two little spotted kiwi, one of which, a hybrid (little spotted and Okarito brown), was found near Franz Josef on the South Island's West Coast and transferred in 1993. Until identified as a hybrid, it was hailed as something of a miracle — a relict mainland little spotted kiwi. The last known member of its species to inhabit the mainland was recovered in 1938.

The presence of so many little spotted kiwi on Kapiti Island has long been a puzzle. No one can be sure whether

they arrived naturally (when sea levels were lower and the island was connected to the mainland about 12,000 years ago) or whether they were purposefully introduced, before or after the arrival of Europeans. Perhaps both scenarios apply. Little spotted kiwi certainly thrive on Kapiti, and whenever birds have been transferred away, their territories have quickly been taken up by other birds.

During incubation, the male little spotted kiwi is the sitter. He covers the nest entrance, especially early on in the incubation period. He may even take concealment a step further by tossing leaves over his tracks near the burrow. Little spotted kiwi lay one or two eggs per season. They sometimes relay if the first clutch fails.

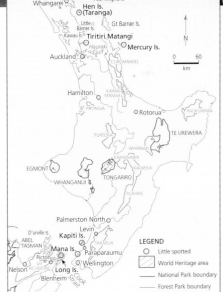

Great spotted kiwi

Apteryx haastii

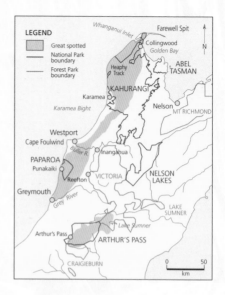

LEGEND
- Great spotted
- National Park boundary
- Forest Park boundary

Whanganui Inlet · Farewell Spit · Collingwood · Golden Bay · Heaphy Track · ABEL TASMAN · KAHURANGI · Karamea · Karamea Bight · Nelson · MT RICHMOND · Westport · Cape Foulwind · Buller R. · Inangahua · PAPAROA · Punakaiki · Reefton · VICTORIA · NELSON LAKES · Greymouth · Grey River · LAKE SUMNER · Lake Sumner · Arthur's Pass · ARTHUR'S PASS · CRAIGIEBURN

0 — 50 km

MĀORI NAME: Roa

HEIGHT: 45 cm

AVERAGE WEIGHT: Female 3.3 kg, male 2.4 kg

DESCRIPTION: Brownish-grey plumage overall, mottled or banded transversely white, with a ginger tinge. The plumage is soft to touch. The bill is light horn, its average length is 12 cm in females, and 10 cm in males. The iris is black. The legs and feet are pale brown to light grey.

DISTRIBUTION: North-west Nelson, North Westland, Paparoa Range, the Southern Alps from Arthur's Pass area to Lake Sumner

HABITAT: Native forest, subalpine shrubland, grassland and herbfield

STATUS: Endangered. The population is projected to halve in three generations.

Great spotted kiwi are the mountaineers of the kiwi family. They tend to live in upland forest and subalpine shrubland and grassland, with North-west Nelson and Kahurangi National Park supporting the largest numbers. They also occupy the forested hills north-east of Westport, the Paparoa Range, and mountainlands flanking the Southern Alps from the Arthur's Pass area north to the headwaters of North Canterbury's Hurunui River and the hills and valleys near Lake Sumner. Territories also occur in the head of the Taramakau Valley, which saddles with the Hurunui at Harper Pass.

Kiwi surveys in the Hurunui area in recent times have found a few pairs of great spotted kiwi living in isolation on the Puketeraki Range east of the Southern Alps. They were found about 15 km east of previously known territories. Trampers on the Heaphy Track, which traverses Kahurangi National Park between Golden Bay and the West Coast,

frequently hear the calls of great spotted kiwi, especially around the Gouland Downs.

Great spotted kiwi females in prime condition reach weights of 4 kg, which is about as heavy as kiwi get, although as a species they have a shorter, stouter and straighter bill than brown kiwi. It appears that great spotted kiwi have always been confined to the southern regions of New Zealand, certainly in the past few thousand years.

As a rule, great spotted kiwi lay just one egg. Perhaps because the female is generally not producing a second egg she takes part in the incubation, taking over from the male halfway through the night. He does most of the day shift. Great spotted kiwi nest burrows may have more than one entrance.

CHAPTER 3

Tāne's bird

Māori contact

Without predatory mammals to contend with, kiwi proliferated on the islands of New Zealand — the last temperate landmass in the world to be discovered and inhabited by humans. At its peak, the kiwi population no doubt outnumbered New Zealand's present human population, probably by several million. Kiwi were found throughout the land, from coastal dunelands to subalpine grasslands. Dense jungle-like forest was their preferred

Right: A rare pure white North Island brown kiwi. The feathers of these kiwi were highly prized for cloak making.

Creation stories

Those first settlers would have found the kiwi strangely different from the birds of tropical eastern Polynesia. Not surprisingly, kiwi were woven into Māori creation stories and traditions. Some tribal traditions regard kiwi as the eldest offspring of Tāne Mahuta, god of the forest, whose children are the trees, birds and animals. Whereas on the small oceanic islands of eastern Polynesia, Tangaroa, god of the sea and all its creatures, had been the paramount god, in New Zealand Tāne held sway. The forest, and all components of it, embodied a sacred life force. Kiwi had a special place. Some traditions referred to the kiwi as Te Manuhuna a Tāne, the Hidden Bird of Tāne. The nocturnal habits and shy character of kiwi would have produced such a title. The expression took on proverbial meaning. It could apply to people who turned up unexpectedly. The kiwi's speed through the bush inspired an incantation that was used by those who wanted to be fleet-footed, such as someone trying to escape enemy pursuers.

Above: John Keulemans, North Island Kiwi, 1888.

habitat, and it covered almost 80 percent of the land 1000 years ago as Polynesian emigrants from South Pacific tropical islands began arriving on great ocean-going waka.

Besides its unusual appearance, the kiwi must have seemed a mysterious creature. How could early Māori explain the discovery at night of burrows containing one or two enormous eggs that remained in the nest for weeks on end but with no bird in the vicinity and the burrow entrances partly covered up? Wondrous stories emerged. Kiwi eggs, according to one account from the North Island, remained so long in the nest that roots grew over them.

Due to its standing in the family of Tāne, kiwi gained a tapu status, a sacredness. But in order to survive, early Māori needed to hunt, and kiwi were among the birds they hunted for meat and feathers. Kiwi hunting was governed by prescribed rituals, practices and prohibitions. Kiwi meat was the food of the chiefs in some tribal traditions, and a chief could claim exclusive hunting rights over a designated area of forest — a rahui kiwi. Breaches of the rahui could end in bloodshed. Of course, moa were larger and more satisfying targets for meat collectors. A single bird could feed a family for some days.

Kiwi hunting parties had to take great care not to offend tapu. It might mean, for example, the departure of birds and other resources to a part of the forest that was controlled by a rival tribe or family. To ensure the good health and fruitfulness of the forest, Māori would deploy a talisman or mauri, often a special stone. It was placed in the forest to act as a resting place for the gods. Hunting parties might call on the services of a tohunga, a priest-like person with specialist knowledge, to bless their expedition and provide guidance. Karakia, or prayers, were recited to improve hunting

Above: Three young women wearing kiwi cloaks.

prospects. Much importance was attached to food and its preparation in advance of an expedition. In some tribes, hunters would fast the day before; some might not take cooked food with them.

Kiwi hunting parties usually took with them an invaluable aid — dogs. Kuri had been introduced from eastern Polynesia. On a hunt they might be walked on a leash. Sometimes rattles fashioned from hardwood, shell or bones were hung around the neck of the kuri to enable the hunters to follow if the dog happened on a scent. Muzzles were fitted to kuri to prevent undue damage to the kiwi or if live capture was intended. Experienced kuri grew to be wary of the sharp scything feet of a cornered kiwi.

Kahukiwi weaving

The weaving of kahukiwi was a particular art form, and it continues to be practised by a few chosen weavers utilising feathers from kiwi that have been found dead. The delicate feathers are knotted into the flax backing so that the inside of the feather, which faced the body of the kiwi, was turned outwards on the cloak. This preserved the ruffled splendour of kiwi plumage. In the past, white feathers from albino or semi-albino kiwi were sometimes incorporated. Some cloaks carried up to 10,000 feathers; some had only borders of kiwi feathers. These days kahukiwi are normally only seen in museums or at ceremonial occasions on Māori marae.

Right: North Island brown kiwi feathers.

Fowling was carried out day or night. During the day, the hunters relied on finding kiwi in their burrows or shelters. The best times, though, were often just on dusk and in the first few hours of darkness. In the fading light, the hunters could look out for kiwi tracks or probe holes and mark them with ponga leaves, silver side up. To assist night hunting, torches were used. They were often made of rimu bark, which glowed without bursting into flame. The idea was to trick kiwi into thinking that the glow was from a biophosphorescent forest worm. As the bird rushed forward to capture the worm, the fowler set the dog free to seize the kiwi. An agile hunter might also attempt to catch a kiwi by hand.

Rituals accompanied the first kill, typically karakia acknowledging the bountifulness of the forest and its attendant gods. Birds were cooked in various ways, mainly spit-roasted over an open fire or steamed in an umu or underground oven. Cooked birds were often stored in their own fat and transported in kete (baskets) made of woven flax. Traps or spring-snares were also used to capture kiwi. Other birds, such as weka and kereru, were also hunted in this way.

Kiwi provided more than meat. Kiwi leg bones were sometimes crafted into koauau nose flutes. The feathers were coveted for cloaks — the precious kahukiwi. A spectacular garment, the kiwi feather cloak was usually made for a high-ranking person. It took many kiwi to make a full-length cloak. Such a cloak became an heirloom. It was nearly always named and the names were carefully transmitted through the generations. Kahukiwi evoked prestige and high status not only because of their beauty but also because they carried the spirit of the bird itself. Kiwi lived close to the earth, close to Papatuanuku, the earth mother, who was also Tāne's mother.

European contact

Europeans greeted the first tantalising glimpse of the kiwi —
a skin — with a mixture of surprise and scepticism. This first
skin, from a brown kiwi, came into the hands of an English
mariner, Captain Barclay, of the ship *Providence,* in Sydney
in 1811. Barclay, who was involved in transporting British
convicts to Australia, carried the skin back to England where
it was acquired by George Shaw, Assistant Keeper of
Zoology at the British Museum. Shaw named the strange
bird *Apteryx australis,* a perceptive choice because the name
survives to this day notwithstanding attempts soon after-
wards to associate the bird with penguins and even the
extinct dodo.

Frustrated by a continuing lack of evidence for the
existence of the kiwi, the London Zoological Society issued
an appeal for specimens. A New Zealand missionary teacher
William Yate sent off a skin to London via Sydney in March
1834. It was of a North Island brown kiwi, apparently the
second he had seen alive. Yate not only supplied a
specimen. He also supplied a ground-breaking account of
the kiwi's appearance, feeding habits and other behaviour.

When the Treaty of Waitangi was signed in 1840 and New
Zealand formally became a British colony, the bird destined
to be the national emblem was still something of an enigma.
Only the brown kiwi had been described. Already there was
concern about the declining kiwi numbers and distribution.
New Zealand Company naturalist Ernst Dieffenbach, who
obtained only one specimen during a stay of 18 months in
New Zealand, reported that kiwi were disappearing as a
result of predation by dogs and cats.

By 1893, a number of naturalists had identified and

First illustration

The first attempt at drawing the kiwi was less
successful than George Shaw's description. An
engraving by R.P. Nodder, which appeared in *The
Naturalist's Miscellany,* depicted a slender upright bird
in reddish-brown plumage. The stance and body shape
were astray of the mark but the bird's head, bill and
feet were fairly portrayed by Nodder, who of course
had no experience of live kiwi. Some naturalists were
flummoxed and demanded proof of the bird's
existence.

described three species and two sub-species. Whereas in the
centuries before European settlement Māori hunted and ate
tens of thousands of moa and undoubtedly hastened their
extinction, a new era of plunder, directed at kiwi,
accompanied the arrival of European explorers, surveyors,
bush rangers, prospectors and bird collectors.

Without access to corner stores or supermarkets, the new
settlers helped themselves to what the bush had to offer.
Nineteenth-century accounts of the hunting, cooking and
taste of kiwi almost overshadow descriptions of the bird's
strange biology and behaviour.

William Yate, the Anglican missionary who produced the
long-awaited specimen for London, wrote in 1835 that the
flesh of the kiwi was 'black, sinewy, tough and tasteless'.
Opinions varied, however. A later missionary, Richard
Taylor, declared the kiwi 'good eating'. He wrote in 1855
that it 'tastes more like tender beef than bird; the principal
fleshy parts are the ribs and legs'.

Pioneer surveyors were also among those who came upon
kiwi meat. Short of food in Taranaki in the 1870s, Thomas

Above: Thomas Henry Potts, the Canterbury naturalist, proudly poses with a stuffed kiwi.

Skinner dined on kiwi. He thought it tasted at first like fish then, the next day, like wild boar. His appetite, he said, was affected by the thought of the kiwi's staple food, worms.

When the value of capturing kiwi for museums, scientific collections and a developing trade in kiwi feathers became known, professional collectors, assisted by dogs, tracked kiwi with the resolve of bounty hunters. Walter Buller noted that a kiwi was easily 'brought to earth' by an experienced birding dog. Wrote Buller: 'a hundred or more have been taken in this way in the course of a single night.'

Thomas Potts, the Canterbury naturalist, confirmed the plunder, noting further that dogs belonging to miners and prospectors destroyed 'great numbers, far more than either they or their owners consume'. William Docherty, who collected the first great spotted kiwi specimens, reported to Potts in 1872 that he had killed about 2200 kiwi, both brown and grey. Many of these kiwi were slaughtered not for their scientific or museum interest but for their feathers — 'kiwi fur'. Little spotted kiwi skins were of particular value, contributing to fashionable accessories, including trimmings on hats and dresses. In Europe, kiwi 'fur' muffs were in demand for a time.

Commercial exploitation of kiwi was outlawed in 1896 when they were legally protected. Attention could now turn to valuing kiwi for their unique role in the avifauna not only of New Zealand but of the bird world at large.

Kiwi lifestyle

Social life

Once, the popular image of the kiwi was that it led a largely solitary and socially deprived life. Poor kiwi, blundering about the forest floor on its own, with the male bird sentenced to solitary confinement on the nest for months on end. But research into ways of conserving kiwi is turning up surprising new information about the way kiwi interact with each other. Behaviour varies between the species and even within species, according to their habitat.

Stewart Island birds are the most socially advanced. They breed in stable groups of three to five mature adults and a similar number of juveniles. It is likely the members of each group are related. Family groups seem to survive in territories of about five hectares in the mosaic of duneland, copper tussock grassland, shrubland and low forest that makes up the Mason Bay area. Male and female birds share incubation, and sometimes others in the group help out. In one case, a grown offspring was observed relieving its parents on the nest.

Sharing incubation does seem to be a trait of South Island kiwi. Great spotted kiwi, Okarito browns and Haast tokoeka also co-operate at nesting time, with both adults sharing incubation. Only among the North Island browns and little spotted kiwi does the male do the bulk of the incubation.

Kiwi are relatively long-lived birds. A lifespan of up to 40 years is possible (achieved by a bird in captivity) but an average somewhere between 10 and 20 years for birds in the wild is probably nearer the mark.

Kiwi are monogamous and pairs can last a lifetime. Males are sexually mature by about 18 months, but females generally do not lay until they are between three and five years old.

Territory

Kiwi are territorial. Territory size varies enormously. On Kapiti Island, little spotted kiwi live at high densities, with territories cheek by jowl and as small as 1.6 hectares. In Hawke's Bay hill country, the size of North Island brown kiwi territories reach 40 hectares, and on the South Island West Coast, some Haast tokoeka territories have been estimated at 100 hectares. This equates to some 150 football fields — a vast area for a flightless bird to patrol.

Kiwi territory size means that, to be healthy and self-supporting, most populations require very large areas. A self-supporting population of North Island brown kiwi might need an area in the order of 15,000 hectares.

Kiwi are not fussy about framing territories around geographical features like steep slopes and streams or rivers. They are cross-country specialists. Using their claws as crampons, they will negotiate terrain of extraordinary steepness.

In the course of night-time foraging, kiwi may travel long distances, over a kilometre. Normally they have a rather slow and plodding gait but they can accelerate quickly if alarmed or if they need to react to an intruder in their territory.

Above: A pair of Okarito brown kiwi probing sphagnum bog for invertebrate food.

A territory is usually a kiwi's sovereign patch. It is defended fiercely — to the death if necessary. Once the territory is established, its owner usually stays bound to it for life. Numerous nesting burrows, dens and shelters will be built in a territory and the resident kiwi and his mate will occupy different sites on different days, rotating their accommodation as if to spread their influence. In North-west

Swimming champs

Great spotted kiwi in the Saxon River of North-west Nelson, fitted with radio transmitters, were found to routinely cross the river, which in normal flows is a large stream too deep for them to wade. A radio-tagged North Island brown kiwi astounded researchers by swimming the Whanganui River, which is many times larger than the Saxon River. At different times the bird swam across and back.

Nelson, great spotted kiwi were found to use up to 100 dens per territory. They tended to use a different one each day.

Whereas kiwis usually dig their burrows, they can use rotting logs, toetoe bushes, clumps of gahnia or similarly thick vegetation for their dens or shelters.

To reinforce their tenure of a territory, kiwi are thought to use their slightly acrid-smelling faeces as markers, as do some territorial mammals.

At one time it was thought only male kiwi held territories and that females became attached to them. However, females have also been discovered holding territories. One study showed that bonded pairs spent only about 40 percent of days sleeping together.

Right: An Okarito brown kiwi's burrow at the base of a stump covered in moss and kidney fern.

Aggression

Both male and female kiwi may be actively involved in territory defence but the male is more likely to take on intruders. Border fights are seldom observed but they are said to be no-holds-barred affairs of kicking and scratching, accompanied by hoarse, guttural calls.

Austrian collector Andreas Reischek, who explored New Zealand wilderness areas between 1877 and 1889, documented a fight between two male North Island brown kiwi in the King Country:

> The fight was a combination of sabre duel and boxing match. They attacked each other ferociously with their bills, so that the feathers flew from their breasts; and they rose up on one leg, letting fly at one another with their sharp-clawed feet. In their excitement they pawed the ground and uttered grunting noises.

Charlie Douglas, the legendary South Westland explorer/philosopher, wrote in the late 1890s:

> Harmless as they appear, they can still kill each other but they could not be called quarrelsome birds, unless a few from different holes are put in the same cage, then there is war.

Small but feisty

Southern tokoeka and Okarito brown kiwi are especially aggressive, even with human intruders. If sufficiently provoked, they will charge at humans and crash into their legs. It is possible these kiwi confront and see off animals such as deer in their territories.

The kiwi call

Besides using dens and perhaps their droppings, kiwi appear to stake out territories with their calls — shrill, penetrating calls, described by ornithologist Walter Buller as 'half-whistle, half scream'. Such calls can carry up to a kilometre on a still night in semi-open country.

The standard call for territory vigilance, contact with a mate or advertisement for one, in brown kiwi species and tokoeka species, is a series of rising notes, each ending with a short sharp descending note. Each note lasts about two seconds and is usually repeated 10 to 25 times. Male calls are higher-pitched. The female brown kiwi's call is hoarser than the male's, described by one researcher as like the heaving noise a cat makes before it vomits.

The hallmark calls of the great spotted and little spotted kiwi involve an ascending warble, repeated several times. The great spotted kiwi calls are delivered with impressive power and the sound carries a long way — 'Crrruick!'. The female has a slower, more throaty call than the male. Little spotted kiwi calls, somewhat similar to those of the great spotted, are faster and high-pitched.

In all kiwi species most of the contact calling is done by the male, which can call up to three times more often than the female. Sometimes the pair will strike up a duet while foraging near each other or patrolling territory. Peak calling occurs in mid-winter at the onset of the breeding season. Call rates are at a low in February. The first few hours of darkness are when most calling is done, although calls can occur at any time of night. Moonlight seems to inhibit the kiwi voice.

Above: A male North Island brown kiwi issuing a territorial call at Otorohanga's Kiwi House.

Calls to warn off an intruder are raucous, intense and intimidating. They mean business. Instead of an ascending note, the anger calls comprise harsh descending notes, loudly and rapidly delivered.

Other sounds

At close quarters, kiwi may utter other sounds, ranging from grunts and growls to bill-clacking, murmurs and chortles. Chicks squeal when alarmed; adults sometimes hiss when handled. While probing soil and sifting through leaf litter kiwi commonly snort to clear the dirt from their nostrils.

Breeding

The kiwi breeding pattern is unlike that of other birds. Peculiarities include the size of the egg, the length of incubation, the reliance on the male alone (in some varieties) to incubate, and the early independence of the chicks. Breeding effort is geared to producing chicks that are active and able to feed for themselves within a matter of days.

Nest selection and lining of the nest is thought to be mainly the task of male kiwi. The chosen burrow is not necessarily the deepest, in fact often the nest burrows of North Island brown kiwi are shorter than their regular day-time shelters, and the sitting bird and egg may even be visible from the outside. Kiwi use their powerful feet to dig the burrow, which is often not used, as a nest at least, until vegetation has grown round the entrance and the excavated soil blends in with the surroundings. The art of camouflage is well practised by kiwi.

Two or three weeks before laying, the pair will mate. Foreplay is initiated by the male. He will tap or stroke the female on the back of her neck with his bill. If the female is receptive she will crouch with her bill resting on the ground and neck and head extended. The male mounts her. To keep his balance without the use of wings, he grasps her back feathers. Copulation is brief, with the whole procedure lasting only a few minutes.

At their peak weight just before breeding, the female usually needs to use reserves of body fat to manufacture the egg because of its huge size. She loses more weight by not eating during the last few days before laying. Females on the point of laying waddle about looking uncomfortable. Some

Above: Courtship behaviour by a pair of great spotted kiwi at the Otorohanga Kiwi House.

Gymnastic performance

Not much is known about courtship display. Males in captivity, however, have been observed performing all kinds of gymnastic stunts in their enclosures just before the breeding season — rolling, leaping and hopping, even lying on their backs kicking their feet in the air!

Above: A two-week-old Okarito brown kiwi chick leaves its nest burrow. It is carrying a tiny radio transmitter.

even stand in water, perhaps to relieve the weight on their legs or to cool down.

Laying occurs from May to February, depending on species and location. Winter, spring and summer seasons are involved, and conditions can range from freezing temperatures and snow covering the burrow, as for Haast tokoeka in winter and early spring, to subtropical heat and humidity as for Northland brown kiwi.

The male bird gradually loses weight during breeding. Over the incubation period, he will not spend quite as many hours feeding, and close to hatching time he may remain at the nest for a couple of nights. He sits on the egg through the daylight hours and heads out to feed around dusk, throwing twigs and leaves roughly across the burrow entrance to disguise it.

Incubation takes about 80 days but it may span anything from 70 to 85 days, depending on the species, location and factors such as the temperature in the nest. By any measure, it is an extraordinarily long time. Few bird species in the world come anywhere near two and a half months' incubation. By comparison, weka, another flightless bird of the New Zealand forest, have an incubation lasting 26 to 28 days. Sitting times for kiwi in one breeding season become marathon efforts when second or third clutches are involved.

Heat control

Unlike most of the world's birds, North Island brown kiwi and the little spotteds leave their eggs unattended for hours at a stretch in the cool of the night. The temperature regime inside a kiwi egg has long fascinated scientists, and new information about temperatures and egg turning is coming to light as a result of intensive monitoring of North Island brown kiwi nests.

This same research is also confirming an appalling failure rate of eggs, as high as 70 percent in some populations. Some eggs fail because they are infertile or broken or eaten by predators. Some are invaded by bacteria through the pores and end up addled. Some are deserted by the incubating bird, for unknown reasons.

Male kiwi everywhere and the females of the southern species develop brood patches. These are bare areas of skin on the underside of the bird and the inside of its thighs. Brood patches enable the adult to more effectively transfer body heat to the developing embryo in the egg and later to the chick in the first few days after hatching.

At hatching, the shell is cracked open by the chick. To achieve this, it has to stab the shell with its miniature bill (it has no egg tooth) and push hard with its feet. It wriggles clear, exhausted but open-eyed and well-feathered. Its belly is swollen by a generous yolk sac, and for the first few hours the chick is a clumsy bundle, lying silently in the nest with its wet feathers drying slowly. The yolk sac nourishes the chick through its first day or two when it tries wobbling to its feet, bow-legged because of its bulging tummy.

Neither parent is inclined to bring food. The father offers the new-born warmth and protection at the nest but not around the clock. At night he wanders off to feed, leaving the chick unguarded. Kiwi chicks emerge from eggs as miniature adults, fully feathered. They are ready to feed in the way adults do within a few days. Although in body size they are only about a fifth that of adults, their bills and legs are proportionately well developed, being a third to a half the size of adults. By the end of the first week the chick ventures out to feed by itself, usually at night. After 10 days it is gone from the nest for hours at a time, still foraging alone and without training.

North Island brown kiwi chicks set out foraging two to five days after hatching. At an age of three to five weeks they are fully independent juveniles. By six weeks they have doubled their 300 g hatching weight. Juveniles in an ideal habitat may reach adult weights in 10 or 12 months, but many of them take longer.

Little spotted kiwi chicks are known to feed in the twilight of dusk and until shortly after dawn. Like brown kiwi chicks, they are small replicas of their parents and become independent very quickly. As time goes by, the parents become less tolerant of the youngster, which must explore the wider world and eventually seek a mate and territory of its own. On Stewart Island, the pattern is quite different. There, young tokoeka live with their parents and older siblings.

Unfortunately, the mortality rate among kiwi chicks is exceptionally and tragically high. A large number are killed by predators. Although chicks under three months of age favour dense vegetation, they tend to 'freeze' rather than flee a predator as if acting out a predator-response instinct appropriate to prehistoric times but not today. In the distant past their predators, notably large raptors, hunted by sight

Above: The beak of a hatching North Island brown kiwi chick breaks through the shell.

Above: The shell splits, revealing a tight package of wet feathers and pink flesh.

Above: The hatchling wriggles free, with bill and feet as pink as its exposed skin.
Right: The newly hatched chick soon dries off and looks alert.

Opposite page: The father broods the new chick.

and sound. Today, introduced killers use scent as well as sight and sound.

The breeding strategy of kiwi, however laborious it might seem in light of current conservation concerns, did work well in the past, allowing kiwi to spread throughout New Zealand and occupy an array of habitats. Among the birds of New Zealand they were supremely successful.

The eccentric egg

Of all that is strange about the life and times of kiwi, the egg is perhaps the most eccentric element. Around the world, the kiwi egg is renowned for its great size. Someone once jested that the bird is simply the kiwi egg's way of making more eggs!

There is a purpose to it all. Kiwi produce large eggs not to astound the world or create records but to end up with chicks that are raring to go within a few days of hatching. This saves the adults from having to commit weeks to brooding and feeding duties — which is the case with most other bird species.

In other words, kiwi invest in the next generation primarily through the large egg size and long incubation. The main focus of this strategy is the yolk. It represents a massive 60 to 65 percent of the egg's volume and some 90 percent of the in-built energy. Being yolk-rich, the egg it is able to produce a chick prepared to venture outside the nest at an extraordinarily early age.

Above: Heavy with egg — an x-ray of a North Island brown kiwi the day before she laid her egg.

Egg sizes

The egg of North Island brown kiwi, southern tokoeka and great spotted kiwi weighs about 430 g when laid — approaching the weight of a pack of butter. At about 125 mm long and 78 mm in diameter, it is a real handful. In the North Island brown kiwi, a second egg is already forming in the female's other ovary as the first egg is laid. At the laying of the first egg, the second measures about 40 mm in diameter and weighs 350 g. Little spotted kiwi lay a smaller egg (300 g, 110 mm long and about 70 mm in diameter) but it can reach almost a quarter of the weight of the bird itself — a phenomenal feat.

The eggshell plays its own part. It is porous, allowing for an exchange of water out and oxygen in. Bacteria may be admitted as well, though, and the nastier microbes can endanger the embryo and cause the egg to go rotten. Bacteria certainly have a nice rich yolk to nestle in and a long period in which to build a culture. As in the eggs of other birds, the egg white or albumen of kiwi eggs fends off an invasion by microbes. Although designed for a long incubation, the shell is relatively thin and may be fatally cracked by a careless sitting bird. On the other hand, the egg's thinness enables the hatchling to split it open fairly easily.

The chick is a miniature marvel when it does emerge, having benefited by the effort of the adults to bring it into the world well developed. Odd though it may seem, kiwi adults do their parenting before the arrival of their offspring.

Kiwi 'tucker'

Except for the Stewart Islanders and juveniles, kiwi feed during the hours of darkness. Equipped with a spear-like nose, they rely largely on their sense of smell to locate food but also utilise their eyes and ears. Legs and feet are used to enable the bird to get about rather than to scratch in the leaf litter as domestic fowl and other birds do. The bill is all-important.

Typically, the foraging kiwi keeps its head lowered and the tip of the bill near the ground. It walks purposefully, tapping, prodding and sniffing with its bill until it finds a spot worth probing. It forages and checks out strange objects using nostrils at the tip of a curiously long bill. It will even lift its head and sniff the air, in the manner of some mammals, if it encounters something unfamiliar in its territory.

Because the tip of the upper mandible overlaps the lower one, the 'nostrils' are protected as the bill is thrust into the soil. Nasal valves also operate in a protective way. Probe holes vary from neatly drilled openings the diameter of the bill to funnel-shaped holes up to 15 cm deep and 10 cm wide at the surface. Such funnels indicate a feverish amount of digging for invertebrate prey. Kiwi can bore into the soil with a corkscrewing or levering action, and they have been seen almost to achieve a 'headstand', feet in the air, while pursuing food deep down. They will bury their bill to the hilt at these times.

Worms are at the top of the menu. Kiwi are adept at catching worms. Experiments suggest they can smell or hear worms moving through the soil at depths of up to 30 mm. Of course, they can probe much deeper. Kiwi have a wide choice of worms — 178 native species and 14 introduced species. Some of the large native worms phosphoresce or glow as they are prised from the soil. At night the glow can be strong enough to illuminate the kiwi's face and bill. Kiwi land their catch with the dexterity of an angler trying to net a large fat trout on a line with low breaking strain. Walter Buller was impressed:

> It is amazing to observe the extreme care and deliberation with which the bird draws the worm from its hiding place, coaxing it out as it were by degrees, instead of pulling or roughly breaking it.

When it comes to feeding, kiwi are primarily carnivorous. They will eat just about any insect or invertebrate animal encountered in the course of flicking through leaf litter or probing the ground. But they do have their favourite foods.

Above: A female tokoeka foraging on Ocean Beach, Stewart Island.

After worms, they are keen on beetle grubs and beetle adults, spiders, caterpillars, centipedes, millipedes, snails, cicada nymphs, ants, native cockroaches, woodlice (slaters) and weta, a large New Zealand member of the cricket family.

There is a vegetarian component to the kiwi diet. Berries and seeds are eaten reasonably often. The fruits of miro, hinau, kahikatea and totara trees as well as those of various coprosma and hebe shrubs are known to appeal to kiwi. Grass seed and fern spores, even leaves, are also ingested, accidentally or otherwise. To find out what the birds have been eating, scientists analyse kiwi droppings or examine the stomach contents of kiwi accidentally killed.

The most intensive studies on kiwi feeding habits have been carried out on little spotted kiwi on Kapiti Island, where the birds, in addition to probing the soil, push and wriggle their bills through the leaf litter at a relatively flat angle as if sifting it.

Above: This tokoeka's beak is almost completely submerged in the sand as it probes for food.

A kiwi's water needs are satisfied mainly through the water content of the food it eats but when a kiwi does drink from a stream, pond or puddle it immerses its bill then tips its head back. The water goes down with a gurgle. Kiwi gizzards sometimes contain grit and small pebbles, which serve to aid digestion.

Lobster snack

Larger prey include an occasional frog and koura (freshwater lobster) where they are available. Kiwi mainly seem to prey on koura up to about 10 cm long when the koura crawl on to stream banks during floods. The ability of kiwi to wade and swim, however, suggests they may even at times 'fish' for koura in the shallows. To ingest a newly caught food item the kiwi will flip it from the tip of its bill into its gullet in a movement so swift the food is merely a blur.

Hazards

A dult kiwi are generally rough, tough and resilient. They are relatively long-lived and breed steadily if slowly. In pre-human New Zealand, between the ice ages when forest covered more than three-quarters of the land, kiwi multiplied with few impediments. Extrapolations from present-day distributions and territory size suggest there could have been as many as 12 million kiwi at one time.

Since the arrival of humans and the introduction of exotic animals, however, kiwi numbers have plummeted. Kiwi face many kinds of hazards. Given the combined impact of these hazards, it is a wonder that kiwi have a foothold on mainland New Zealand at all.

Stoats

At the top of the hazards list is the stoat. The introduction of stoats from Britain is now regarded as an unmitigated disaster for New Zealand's indigenous wildlife — birds, lizards, frogs and the larger insects. Although two other members of the mustelid family, the ferret and weasel, were also brought here from Europe, stoats spread more widely and across more habitats than the others.

Kiwi chicks left alone by parents are especially vulnerable to stoat attacks. When challenged by a stoat, the kiwi chick may growl, kick and bill-snap but is too small to resist an attack for very long. Yet nowhere in New Zealand do stoats

Kiwi Populations		
Variety	1998	2006 (projected)
North Island brown kiwi	31,000	20,000
Okarito brown kiwi	140	55
Southern tokoeka	26,000	24,000
Haast tokoeka	200	125
Little spotted kiwi	1100	1200
Great spotted kiwi	20,000	12,000
Total kiwi	**78,440**	**57,380**

Enemy number one

Valued as ermine in its European homelands, the stoat is the New Zealand national bird's major enemy.

Stoats now live throughout the North and South Islands (but not Stewart Island) and on some smaller islands close to the mainland. They can exist in any habitat where prey is available. Quick-footed, bold and agile hunters, they prey on birds, birds' eggs, mice, rabbits, lizards and larger insects such as weta. They can swim to and colonise islands up to 1.5 km offshore or just swim over for the day to prospect for food. Day or night, they see very well and they also use sound and smell to locate prey.

Female stoats are capable of killing juvenile kiwi four times their weight. Physically, stoats are like high-revving machines, with a pulse rate of 400 to 500 beats a minute and a respiratory rate of up to 100 breaths a minute, all of which means they live life at a fast pace and require large amounts of food to fuel such a metabolism. They do not live long — just one or two years. To compensate, they reproduce at a rate that far exceeds that of many vulnerable native birds.

There are often up to 10 stoat babies, called kits, in a litter, although the number will depend on the availability of food for the mother. At three to five weeks of age, while still in the nest, they are mated by the resident male. Thus the next generation is assured even before the current year's has left the nest.

depend on young kiwi for survival. Kiwi chicks simply add spice to the smorgasbord of native wildlife at the stoat's disposal. Often young kiwi killed by stoats are found with their brains sucked out and their stomachs opened up. Meaty parts of the bird are often left untouched. Compared to other prey, young kiwi are scarce in most places — a minor food source — and stoats appear to kill them more through instinct than hunger.

Stoats breed once a year, in September and October, and the problem for young kiwi is that most of them have not grown big enough to withstand a stoat attack by the time stoat mothers are feeding to put on condition or are nurturing a bunch of nestlings. Juvenile kiwi need to reach a weight of 800 g to 1 kg before they can stand up to a stoat. In other words, they need to be about three times the weight of a full-grown male stoat to foot it with the predator. It will take six months or more for a juvenile kiwi to reach this threshold weight for survival against stoats.

Several studies have demonstrated the persistent terror stoats represent to kiwi. At Okarito, the Department of Conservation mounted an intensive stoat-trapping programme over a two-year period in the mid-1990s while monitoring a number of pairs of kiwi. Despite the programme not one kiwi chick survived. Stoats are thought to have killed the lot. In the North Island, the picture is similar. A long-term study in the Lake Waikaremoana area of Urewera National Park, mounted jointly by Landcare Research and the Department of Conservation, at first showed a reasonable level of success with stoat control and kiwi chick survival but in the second year, despite sustained trapping, stoats killed nine of 10 monitored chicks.

Stoats, however, meet their match with kiwi over about 1 kg in weight. At a burrow in the Okarito forest monitored by a video camera, a stoat was seen to be hurled from the entrance with such force its feet were clear of the ground. Young kiwi are sitting ducks, though, and the threat of predation is especially real during stoat plague years, which are triggered by increased food supply emanating from a boom seeding season in the beech forest. During such a year in the Waikaremoana forest, stoats reach a density of about 10 per square kilometre. It appears that when they can be reduced to one or two per square kilometre, enough young kiwi will survive to adulthood and maintain the population.

Although stoats were always regarded as a problem for kiwi, the devastating extent of their impact has come to light only through research in the 1990s. Until then, stoats were listed alongside or beneath feral cats and dogs gone wild as leading kiwi killers.

Dogs

Dogs, allowed to run wild, can decimate a kiwi population. The worst case recorded so far occurred in Waitangi Forest in Northland in 1987. As many as 500 kiwi, more than half the local population, were massacred, not by a pack of dogs but by a female German shepherd operating alone. Its owner was never located. The killing spree was discovered only by chance through the work of scientists who happened to be monitoring the Waitangi kiwi at the time. Few of the kiwi killed by the German shepherd were eaten. It survived mainly on possums.

A dog may turn wild if left behind by hunters or allowed to stray too far from a farm or urban setting. It will readily track down a sheltering kiwi through the bird's animal-like scent and rip up its burrow. The kiwi's chest area is weakly protected and easily crushed by a pig hunter's dog. Wild dogs menace Northland kiwi in particular. Of a total of 194 dead kiwi reported to the Department of Conservation and the Whangarei Bird Rescue Centre in Northland between 1990 and 1995, no fewer than 130 — two-thirds — died as a result of dog attacks.

Right: Kiwi tracker dog Gem helps researchers by sniffing out kiwi in their burrows.

Other animal threats

Wild cats are conspicuous on Stewart Island but do not appear to worry the southern tokeka there to the extent that stoats do on the mainland, presumably because of the Stewart Island birds' communal family arrangements and shared security. There are no stoats, ferrets or weasels on Stewart Island.

Elsewhere, wild pigs are a threat to kiwi burrows as they root up the forest floor. More than a few kiwi eggs have probably been destroyed this way. Possums are known to frequent kiwi burrows and possibly they, too, target kiwi eggs. Stoats will make a meal of an unattended kiwi egg but rats — brown, black or the smaller kiore — cannot grip the broad surface of the egg with their teeth and are not heavy or strong enough to break it.

Of greater threat to kiwi eggs is the prospect of bacterial invasion during the long period of incubation. Addling may result. Threats to the kiwi egg, although contributing to a wider picture of population decline, do not pose a problem for kiwi surviving on the mainland in the long run.

Among the kiwi predators of old New Zealand, only the weka has survived. Weka and kiwi evolved together over eons. Although weka remain a threat to kiwi eggs and young chicks, they do not threaten the long-term survival of kiwi populations anywhere.

In the past, many kiwi were maimed or killed in possum traps but with the replacement of the notorious gin trap by more humane equipment, fewer kiwi fall victim now. Although possum-poisoning operations involving cyanide

Above: Conservation officer Tony Perry (left) and kiwi scientist Rogan Colbourne discuss the assembly of tracking tunnels as part of stoat-control work in the Haast region of South Westland.

bait and 1080 poison drops might seem hazardous for kiwi, monitoring of kiwi populations in areas where poison drops have occurred indicate kiwi are not at risk so long as precautionary measures are taken when baits are laid.

Habitat destruction

Kiwi habitat continues to be destroyed, although not on the scale seen in the nineteeth century. Some North Island shrubland areas that are home to kiwi are burnt, bulldozed or roller-crushed. Although indigenous forest may now be logged only on a sustainable basis, this may still threaten kiwi habitat.

The cropping of exotic pine plantations for timber is also hazardous for North Island brown kiwi populations that choose to inhabit them. With the roof of their homes removed, some kiwi move on to occupy adjacent stands of forest; others simply make do in the cleared compartments of forest. Any burning of the 'slash' in the logged compartments, in anticipation of replanting, will almost certainly incinerate kiwi living there. But sensitive forest management can minimise the impacts on kiwi living in pine forests. A 1996 accord signed by the forest industry contains guidelines for protecting kiwi and other wildlife that are threatened by logging and planting work. In advance of burning operations, kiwi may be taken into captivity and released into the wild later.

Roads that run through kiwi habitats are lethal, although there are only a few places where road kills might occur and at such places the authorities have erected warning signs for motorists. The main highway between Canterbury and the West Coast, traversing Arthur's Pass, has long been a problem for great spotted kiwi living in the forest near Arthur's Pass village. Each year, one or two injured or dead birds are handed in. Yellow signs carrying a kiwi silhouette now alert motorists to the possible presence of kiwi on the road at night. There are now also signs in Waipoua Forest in Northland, Tongariro National Park and the road to Okarito.

Sadly, the combined impact of stoats, ferrets, weasels, feral cats, wild dogs, possums and wild pigs will cause the extinction of wild populations of mainland kiwi eventually — unless conservation measures initiated in the 1990s are developed further, properly funded and steadfastly implemented.

During the twentieth century, the total kiwi population has fallen by more than 90 percent — a staggering decline. The present rate of decline, in the order of six percent a year, means that in the absence of effective conservation measures, the population will halve every decade. The key to the recovery of kiwi is the survival of the chicks and juveniles against the onslaught of stoats and other predators.

Above: No match for a dog — this female Stewart Island tokoeka was killed in an attack by an uncontrolled dog.

CHAPTER 6

To the rescue

Research

Driven by the spectre of plummeting populations, kiwi research has gained a sharper focus going into the new century. Not only does the research need to shed more light on kiwi population dynamics, breeding patterns and hazards; it must also somehow devise ways of limiting the slaughter of young kiwi by predators.

For much of the twentieth century, kiwi research was ad hoc. Kiwi as a whole were not considered to be at risk. They lived in remote places, mostly far away from people. What harm could come to them? Even as recently as 1990, conservationists did not have a good idea how many kiwi were left.

Then in 1991 the first Kiwi Recovery Plan began to lift research effort in the field. Through the 1990s, fieldwork developed new strands — and produced some revelations. At the same time, geneticists were identifying new varieties of kiwi. Independent studies using mitochondrial DNA and allozymes found in protein came to the same conclusion — long-standing names for kiwi had to be revised to accommodate new varieties.

It then became clear that Okarito brown kiwi and Haast tokoeka were endangered. The effect was galvanising. There was a sudden and urgent need to embark on fieldwork in

South Westland with a view to protecting these rare kiwi.

Okarito and Haast became new frontiers for kiwi research. At Okarito, Department of Conservation staff set out to count the grey-brown kiwi living in the rainforest-clad valleys and ridges near Franz Josef and map their territories and distribution. Intensive banding, radio-tagging and monitoring work has built up an impressive picture of the life and times of Okarito brown kiwi.

Initial research confirmed what had been found among North Island brown kiwi populations — a high mortality rate among chicks. Although there are no ferrets or dogs to worry the kiwi here, and few wild cats, stoats are at large in the forest. Through the use of video cameras, individual burrows have been monitored over several years — a study that has confirmed that stoats and possums do make predatory visits to kiwi burrows. New moves to understand the Okarito brown kiwi and develop ways to protect them include a close-up group study. It involves attaching bands and transmitters to every bird in the study area.

Meanwhile, further south in Westland, on the Haast Range and adjacent country, conservation staff are monitoring a

Opposite page: DOC ranger Selena Brown weighs a 3 kg female Okarito brown kiwi during monitoring work in South Okarito forest.

Kiwi experiments

In 1996, kiwi researchers tested a new protective measure. From the Okarito population, they removed five young nestlings, three to five days old, and sent them to an aviary at Arahura, near Hokitika, for rearing to juvenile stoat-proof size (about 1 kg). As year-old juveniles, they were released back into the wild at Okarito. There was a major setback. Three of the five juveniles were killed by adult birds incensed by the intrusion of the youngsters into established territories. North Island brown kiwi, although stout defenders of territory, do not generally kill juveniles they encounter. Clearly, the Okarito browns were a grumpier lot.

The research team decided on a different strategy — to rear a crop of chicks in a wild predator-free setting (Motuara Island in the Marlborough Sounds) after allowing them a few weeks' feeding and individual care at the Arahura aviary. In a wild setting, the birds are able to interact more naturally and develop survival skills. By mid-1999, a total of 28 juveniles had been released. None were lost to stoats. The kiwi 'farming' aims to rear 12 chicks a year on Motuara Island.

group of Haast tokoeka. Survey and banding work began in 1990 when they realised the Haast birds were different from the Fiordlanders. The research programme centres on lowland and upland pairs, several of which carry radio transmitters. It aims to discover why Haast tokoeka reach their highest numbers at or above the bushline. Is there less predation by stoats at the higher altitudes? Does the colder environment inhibit stoats?

The most widely distributed kiwi, the North Island brown, has long been a focus for study. Access is comparatively easy in certain areas with roads through a number of populations. With the discovery of regional variation in the species, studies have broadened and intensified in recent years.

Right: Changing the radio transmitter on an Okarito brown kiwi.

Opposite page: DOC ranger Chris Rickard releases a female Okarito brown kiwi after a weigh-in during monitoring work on the endangered Okarito population.

'Operation Nest Egg'

A new strategy was developed in the 1990s to assist breeding in selected populations. Eggs are removed from a number of monitored nests and incubated artificially at approved institutions which have experience in breeding captive kiwi. The chicks are raised in captivity and released back into the wild — where they came from — once they reach a stoat-proof weight, at least 800 g. They need to be big enough to resist stoats while still youthful enough to be tolerated by territorial adults.

Artificial incubation is nothing new; zoos and other institutions holding kiwi have managed it for years. But intervening in this way with wild populations is certainly novel. The biggest challenge has to do with the adjustment of the juveniles to life in the wild. There is also the possibility of diseases acquired in captivity spreading to wild populations.

On the positive side, birds that lose the first egg of the season to Operation Nest Egg may relay, with a chance of adding an additional kiwi to the population. Operation Nest Egg has provided new information about how eggs are managed in the wild through the use of temperature gauges at monitored nests. For example, among North Island brown kiwi, eggs are turned daily by the sitting bird, at least in the early stages of incubation. At one time it was thought the eggs were not turned at all.

Sanctuaries

Recent kiwi research shows very clearly that kiwi need better protection from predators. To this end, sanctuaries have been found on offshore islands, and there is no better demonstration of the benefits than in the case of the little spotted kiwi, whose numbers are increasing in contrast to the relentless decline of the other kiwi species. But predator-free islands of sufficient size are not easy to come by. For South Island kiwi, Fiordland and the Marlborough Sounds harbour the best possibilities, although in the case of, say, Haast tokoeka, the bigger islands on Lakes Wanaka and Wakatipu may prove suitable as refuges. In some cases, kiwi may themselves put other endangered species — for example, native frogs and lizards — at risk. Researchers are proceeding carefully with their sanctuary plans.

Having gained international recognition in previous decades for the techniques of transferring endangered species to island sanctuaries, New Zealand began experimenting with the concept of 'mainland islands' in the late 1990s. It sounds simple enough. Given that endangered species will probably do best if they remain in known habitats and climatic conditions, all that needs to be done is to reduce or eliminate the threats over a specific area, and thus create a 'mainland island'. For smaller areas, this might mean predator-proof fencing but kiwi require areas too large for this to be practical and affordable. The use of exotic forests as sanctuaries may be possible for kiwi in Northland, Coromandel, inland Taranaki and Wanganui.

Right: Kapiti Island, one of the offshore islands where kiwi are protected.

The role of the public

While all this specialised research and in-house pondering go on, there remains a role for the general public. The Department of Conservation, through the Kiwi Call Scheme, encourages people to report kiwi calls, probe holes, feathers and footprints. Information from the public has provided valuable information. Fiordland — remote, rugged and unroaded — remains the least well-documented region. In the North Island, a special effort is made to educate landowners and communities in kiwi country to enhance the habitat, keep dogs and cats under control and contribute to the fieldwork when opportunities arise.

Enterprising and novel though the egg and chick transfers may seem, they can only be stop-gap measures in the long term. The survival of kiwi on the mainland will depend on effective control of predators. Research at Waikaremoana has shown that if the survival rate of juveniles can be lifted from about five percent at present to something over 20 percent then populations will grow.

Recovery

The second Kiwi Recovery Plan, running until 2006, aims to increase kiwi numbers and expand their distribution. That means retaining all mainland populations, and protecting them in their natural habitats. There are studies involving all kiwi varieties, with fourteen banded populations having been set up.

The Kiwi Recovery Programme, set up by DOC, the Royal Forest and Bird Protection Society and the BNZ, provides the expertise and funding to put the plan into action. It started out seeking answers to the most basic questions — how many, where, and what kind — and has since gone on to address the gritty questions surrounding the conservation status of kiwi.

In September 1998, the Royal Forest and Bird Protection Society launched a campaign to galvanise public support and funding for kiwi conservation. Calling its campaign 'Kiwis for kiwis', Forest and Bird aims to secure funding to create 11 large kiwi conservation zones in 11 regions — Northland, Coromandel, Tongaririo/Taupo, Taranaki, Urewera, Wanganui, North-west Nelson, Buller, North Canterbury, Westland and Fiordland. The campaign set a fund-raising target — $10 million a year for 10 years — to be raised through appeals to the business sector, Māori tribes, community organisations and the general public.

Opposite page: A striking new entrance to the Queenstown Kiwi and Birdlife Park was built in 1999. The silhouette of a kiwi has been cut out of steel plate.

Pioneering work

The earliest kiwi conservation efforts go back to the late 1800s in Fiordland. In 1894, an Australian-born naturalist, Richard Henry, was appointed custodian of predator-free Resolution Island in Dusky Sound, New Zealand's first flora and fauna reserve. Henry went arduously about his work, transferring flightless birds to Resolution from the adjacent mainland — mainly kiwi and kakapo. There were two kiwi species, roa (tokoeka) and little spotted kiwi. In the first three years, working alone but for his dog, he caught and transferred an astonishing 474 kiwi and kakapo. Then disaster struck. Henry saw a stoat on the island. He realised stoats were able to swim the waterways from the mainland or other islands. It was the end of a dream. He left Dusky Sound in 1908, disillusioned.

Captive kiwi

To see a kiwi in the wild is a rare experience, and for most people, the only opportunity for viewing the national bird live is behind glass at a kiwi house or zoo. Such institutions are allowed to keep and display kiwi so long as they work towards a breeding programme that ensures the captive population is self-sustaining. North Island brown kiwi are predominant in the captive population, which numbers about 75 spread across 15 institutions. Only the Otorohanga Zoological Society holds other species — the great spotted and little spotted kiwi. In the 1990s this institution bred and reared 16 North Island brown, four great spotted and two little spotted kiwi. In light of revelations about genetic variation in North Island brown kiwi, institutions are now careful, when initiating breeding, to match birds from the same region.

Kiwi are not easy to breed in captivity and techniques are always being refined. There continues to be debate, for example, on temperature and humidity settings for birds kept indoors, a topic that is complicated by the fact that individual birds may have different climate tolerances. Studbooks keep track of every bird in captivity, its origins and whether bred in captivity or in the wild. There is strong interest among the institutions for a role in the conservation of threatened wild populations through Operation Nest Egg and/or the captive-rearing of wild chicks and juveniles.

Captive kiwi have contributed a vast amount to the general knowledge of kiwi breeding and other behaviour. For a long time, in the years before radio telemetry, video cameras and night-vision equipment, the finer details of how kiwi lived in the wild were deduced mainly from the study of captive birds.

In the 1970s, nocturnal kiwi houses were introduced. Nocturnal houses reverse the normal day/night sequence so that kiwi are active during the day for the convenience of human visitors. Otorohanga set up its viewing in 1971, Auckland Zoo in 1972 and Wellington Zoo in 1975. All were engaged in breeding programmes and they have all provided other institutions with surplus kiwi over the years.

Otorohanga went a step further by experimenting with the artificial incubation of kiwi eggs. On 10 January 1977, Otorohanga announced a breakthrough — the first chick, a North Island brown, incubated and hatched artificially. It was a television star, with cameras recording the event for both New Zealand and overseas audiences. This heightened the interest of overseas zoos, from whom requests began to flow in for surplus kiwi.

Opposite page: Queenstown Kiwi and Birdlife Park director Paul Wilson displays a five-month-old female brown kiwi chick. Hatched on New year's Day 1997, the chick was the first bred by the institution since it opened in 1986.

Survival of the fittest

From Nga Manu Nature Reserve comes a great survival story. A female North Island brown lived there till she was between 40 and 44 years old — despite being blind. She set an age record for kiwi. Transferred from Wellington Zoo to the Waikanae institution, she kept her keepers well entertained with her aggressive, bossy nature. She would kill other birds that came into her outdoor enclosure, including sparrows, morepork and kereru.

Until she was paired with an eight-year-old male from Auckland Zoo, she gave her mates a hard time. In addition to her longevity, she may have set some sort of record for egg-laying — nine eggs in 18 months at one stage of her life at Nga Manu. Her diet featured regular meals of soaked Biscats, a pelletised protein-rich cat food. She died on New Year's day, 1993.

The current Kiwi Recovery Plan calls on institutions everywhere to be self-sufficient for kiwi stocks. The plan precludes the recruitment by institutions, either in New Zealand or overseas, of any further North Island brown kiwi from the wild. No other varieties of kiwi are available from the wild, either.

In the 1990s, members of the public gained new opportunities to view kiwi in the wild with a guide. On Stewart Island, a tourist operator is permitted to guide visitors to Ocean Beach, a stretch of sand south of Paterson Inlet, where southern tokoeka emerge at night to feed on sandhoppers and other invertebrate life. These kiwi seem not to mind the sound of shutters clicking and voices murmuring adulation. In the north, the introduction of little spotted kiwi to Tiritiri Matangi in the Hauraki Gulf provides limited numbers of overnight visitors to the island with an opportunity at least to hear kiwi calling if not observe them. Tiritiri Matangi is an open sanctuary, a refuge for various endangered species, including takahe and saddleback.

The kiwi is a biological and cultural treasure. It is an identifying symbol world-wide for New Zealand and New Zealanders, and the subject of endless fascination for anyone interested in birds. It deserves as much protection as is necessary to ensure it survives in its various forms.

Opposite page: A little spotted kiwi.

Where to see kiwi

Kaitaia Nocturnal Park, Kaitaia
Northland Regional Museum, Whangarei
Auckland Zoo, Auckland
Otorohanga Kiwi House, Otorohanga
Rainbow and Fairy Springs, Rotorua
NZ Māori Arts and Crafts Institute, Rotorua
Napier Kiwi House, Napier
National Wildlife Centre, Mount Bruce
Nga Manu Nature Reserve, Waikanae
Wellington Zoo, Wellington
Moana Park, West Coast
Orana Wildlife Park, Christchurch
Willowbank Wildlife Reserve, Christchurch
Kiwi and Birdlife Park, Queenstown

Further reading

Billing, Tony ed., *Kiwi Workshop Proceedings*, Auckland Zoo/New Zealand Conservation Management Group, 1998.

Butler, David and John McLennan, *Kiwi Recovery Plan 1991–96*, Department of Conservation, Wellington, 1991.

Fuller, Errol ed., *Kiwis*, SeTo Publishing, Auckland, 1990.

King, Carolyn ed., *The Handbook of New Zealand Mammals*, Oxford University Press, Auckland, 1990.

Buller, W.L., *A History of the Birds of New Zealand*, 2nd ed., published by the author, London, 1888.

Jolly, Jim, *Kiwi — A Secret Life*, New Zealand Natural Heritage Foundation, Massey University, 1991.

McLennan, J.A. et al., *Role of Predation in the Decline of Kiwi,* Apteryx *spp. in New Zealand*, New Zealand Journal of Ecology 20 (1), 1996.

Marchant S. and P.J. Higgins eds, *Handbook of Australian, New Zealand and Antarctic Birds, Vol 1*, Oxford University Press, Auckland, 1990.

Peat, Neville, *The Incredible Kiwi*, Random Century, Auckland, 1990.

Potts, T.H., *Out in the Open*, Lyttelton Times, Christchurch, 1882.

Wolfe, Richard, *Kiwi — More than a Bird*, Random Century, Auckland, 1991.

Robertson, Hugh, *Kiwi Recovery Plan 1996–2006 (draft)*, Department of Conservation, Wellington, 1996.

Index

(italics denote illustrations)

Photograph credits

Rod Morris: pp.3, 7, 9, 11–12 15, 19 top, 22, 27, 31, 33, 37, 45, 46, 53, 57, 68.
Tui de Roy/The Roving Tortoise: pp.10–11, 14, 20, 23, 29, 42, 49, 50, 72.
Department of Conservation: p.19 bottom.
Paul van Klink: pp.24, 25.
Neville Peat: pp.26, 28, 39, 51, 54, 55, 56, 63, 65.
Alexander Turnbull Library: pp.30, 32, 35.
Mark Jones/The Roving Tortoise: pp.38, 41, 43, 59, 60, 61.
Otorohanga Kiwi House: p.47.
Doc Ross: p.67.